# DISNEY'S
# THE ❀ LITTLE
# MERMAID

## "UNDERWATER ENGAGEMENTS"
### PART ONE: ARIEL'S STORY

BOB BUDIANSKY
WRITER

JEFF ALBRECHT
MIKE·DECARLO
STEVE GEORGE
INKERS

HARVEY RICHARDS III
ART CORRECTIONIST

GREGG SANDERSON
ASSOCIATE EDITOR

CARLOS MOTA
PENCILER

TWILIGHT GRAPHICS
COLORISTS

COMICRAFT'S DAVE LAMPHEAR
LETTERER

EVAN SKOLNICK
EDITOR

FABIAN NICIEZA
EDITOR-IN-CHIEF

**DISNEY'S THE LITTLE MERMAID: "UNDERWATER ENGAGEMENTS"** Vol. I, No.1 © 1997 Disney Enterprises, Inc. Published by Acclaim Books, a division of Acclaim Comics, Inc., Fabian Nicieza, President. Office of Publication: 275 Seventh Avenue, New York, NY 10001. Reproduction in whole or in part without written permission from the copyright owner is strictly forbidden. No similarities between any of the names, characters, persons and/or institutions in this magazine with those of any persons living or dead, or any institution is intended and any similarity which may exist is purely coincidental. Acclaim Books and logo is a registered trademark of Acclaim Comics, Inc. ISBN 1-57840-242-5. Printed in the United States of America.

DID YOU SEE *THAT*, *SEBASTIAN*?

WHAT A *STUNNING* DISPLAY OF ATHLETIC ABILITY!

YOU HAVE *OUTDONE* YOURSELF *DIS* TIME, YOUR MAJESTY.

DIS WILL GO DOWN AS DE *GREATEST* SPORTS EVENT IN DE *HISTORY* OF ATLANTICA.

I COULDN'T HAVE DONE IT WITHOUT YOUR HELP, SEBASTIAN.

Oh, YOUR MAJESTY, YOU MAKE ME *BLUSH.*

ON BEHALF OF *MARINE MOTORS*...

...I'D LIKE TO PRESENT YOU WITH YOUR *PRIZE* -- A BRAND NEW *456-SEAHORSE-POWER*, TWIN-CLAM *MUSSEL CAR!*

*THANK YOU!* ALL I CAN SAY IS...

...YOU COULD NOT HAVE PRESENTED IT TO A MORE *DESERVING* MER-PERSON...

WHAT A *SURPRISE*. HIS *EGO* IS EVEN *BIGGER* THAN HIS *MUSCLES*--

...WITH THE POSSIBLE EXCEPTION OF KING TRITON'S DAUGHTER, *ARIEL*...TO WHOM I *DEDICATE* THIS VICTORY.

WHO DOES HE THINK HE IS, TALKING ABOUT YOU LIKE THAT?!

I...I DON'T KNOW.

BUT I WOULDN'T MIND FINDING OUT...

YOUR MAJESTY, PERHAPS YOU SHOULD T'INK TWICE ABOUT LETTING DE TWO OF DEM DRIVE OFF BY *DEMSELVES.*

DESE YOUNG PEOPLE TODAY, DEY GET IN ALL *KINDS* OF TROUBLE! ESPECIALLY *ARIEL!*

Hmmm... I SEE YOUR *POINT,* SEBASTIÁN.

*SEBASTIAN* HAS VOLUNTEERED TO GO ALONG WITH YOU AS YOUR *CHAPERONE.*

*WHAT?!* DAT IS *NOT* WHAT I SAID!

DON'T BE SO *MODEST,* SEBASTIAN! WHEN YOU *HAVE* A GOOD IDEA, YOU SHOULD TAKE *CREDIT* FOR IT!

SO WHERE WOULD YOU LIKE TO *GO*, ARIEL? CORAL CANYON? ANGELFISH FALLS? THE GOLDEN GROTTO?

Hmmm... *ALL* THOSE PLACES SOUND NICE...BUT *I* WAS THINKING OF...

...STINGRAY CITY!

*STINGRAY CITY?!* DE GIRL IS *CRAZY!* DON'T LISTEN TO HER!

ISN'T THAT PLACE SUPPOSED TO BE... *DANGEROUS?*

Oh, THOSE ARE JUST STORIES.

YOU'RE NOT *SCARED,* ARE YOU?

STINGRAY CITY

SCARED? *ME?* NO, OF COURSE NOT. I WAS JUST, um...WORRIED ABOUT *YOU.*

LET'S *ROLL!*

...WHICH IS WHY YOU'RE *NOT* GOING TO TELL HIM.

AFTER ALL, WHO KNOWS WHAT HE'D *DO* TO YOU IF HE FOUND OUT YOU *LET* US COME HERE.

-:*GULP*:- HE'D HAVE ME BACK AT DE *LITTLE MINNOW DAY CARE CENTER* SINGING *"RING AROUND THE GUPPY"* TO A BUNCH OF BAWLING *MER-BABIES!*

I THINK WE'VE SEEN *ENOUGH* OF THIS PLACE.

Oh, AQUARIUS, WE JUST *GOT* HERE. LET'S DO A LITTLE *EXPLORING!*

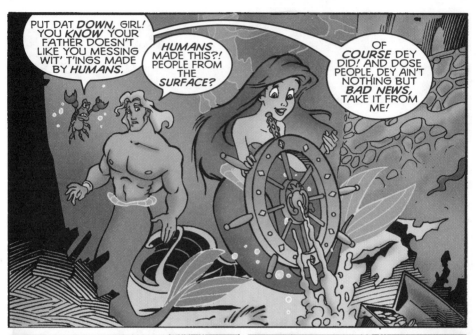

-SIGH-
THAT WAS...
*BEAUTIFUL.*

HE
RISKED
HIS *OWN*
LIFE TO
SAVE
*HERS.*

I'M SO
*HAPPY* THAT
THINGS TURNED
OUT THE WAY
THEY *DID...*

...THE
STINGRAYS
ARE *FRIENDS*
NOW, AND THE
HUMANS ARE
*SAFE...*

# SAVE $10.00 ON

# Disney
## ENCHANTMENT!

**SAVE $10.00 OFF THE RETAIL PRICE WHEN YOU SUBSCRIBE TO DISNEY'S ENCHANTING STORIES! THAT'S LIKE GETTING TWO ISSUES FREE!**

EACH ENCHANTING STORYBOOK FEATURES 64 FULL-COLOR PAGES OF YOUR FAVORITE DISNEY CHARACTERS IN ALL-NEW FUN-FILLED ADVENTURES! ENJOY HOURS OF READING FUN WITH YOUR FRIENDS FROM THE LITTLE MERMAID, BEAUTY AND THE BEAST, POCAHONTAS, HERCULES, 101 DALMATIANS, AND THE HUNCHBACK OF NOTRE DAME!

## YES! PLEASE SEND ME 6 ISSUES OF
## DISNEY'S ENCHANTING STORIES FOR ONLY $17.00.

I UNDERSTAND THAT I'LL SAVE A TOTAL OF $10.00 OFF THE COVER PRICE!

(PLEASE PRINT)

NAME _____

ADDRESS _____

CITY _____

STATE _____ ZIP _____

SEND A CHECK OR MONEY ORDER PAYABLE TO

### ACCLAIM BOOKS

OR CALL 1-888-9-ACCLAIM

FOR VISA AND MASTERCARD ORDERS.

(NY RESIDENTS, PLEASE ADD APPLICABLE SALES TAX.)
PHOTOCOPIES OF THIS FORM ARE ACCEPTABLE.
SORRY - NOT AVAILABLE TO RESIDENTS OF CANADA.

SEND TO:
ACCLAIM BOOKS
YOUNG READER SUBSCRIPTIONS
PO BOX 40
VERNON, NJ 07462

© Disney

KEY CODE 02K

# SAVE $10.00 ON

## ACTION!

# Get 6 Books for the Price of 4!

**Save $10.00 off the retail price when you subscribe to Disney's Action Club! That's like getting two issues FREE! Each Action Club Story features 64 full-color pages of your favorite Disney characters in all-new fun-filled adventures! Enjoy hours of reading fun with your friends from Toy Story, Aladdin, The Mighty Ducks, Hercules, The Lion King, and the Hunchback of Notre Dame.**

## Yes! Please send me 6 issues of Disney's Action Club for only $17.00.

I understand that I'll save a total of $10.00 off the cover price! (Please Print)

Name _____

Address _____

City _____

State _____ Zip _____

Send a check or money order payable to
**Acclaim Books**
**OR CALL 1-888-9-ACCLAIM**
for VISA or MASTERCARD orders.
(NY residents, Please add applicable sales tax.)
Photocopies of this form are acceptable.
Sorry - Not available to residents of Canada.

**Send to:**
**Acclaim Books**
**Young Reader Subscriptions**
**PO Box 40**
**Vernon, NJ 07462**

© Disney

Key code 02K

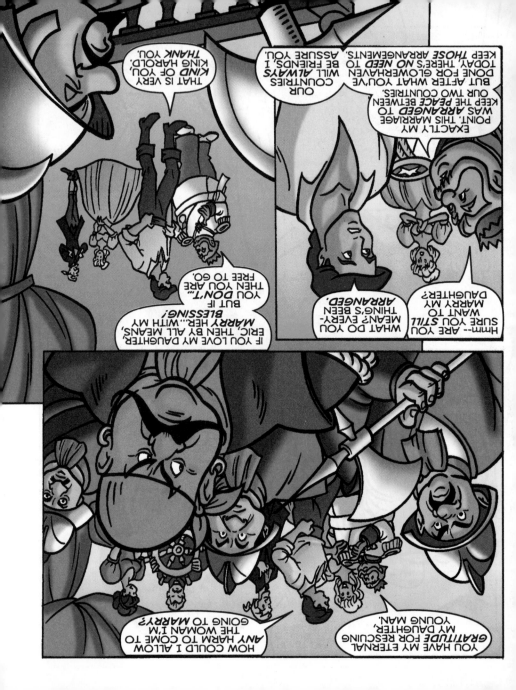

IT'S MORE THAN THAT -- IT'S OUR *LIFELINE!*

ISN'T THAT THE END OF YOUR *SUPPORT ROPE* TRAILING FROM THE *SHIP?*

*WE HAVE TO* GET *BACK* ON THAT SHIP SOMEHOW AND TAKE CARE OF THAT DOUBLE-CROSSING *CAPTAIN CUTLASS!*

BUT... WE CAN'T *FLOAT* HERE IN THE MIDDLE OF *NOWHERE FOREVER.*

*OH MY GOODNESS!* WE'RE BEING *ATTACKED* BY *STINGRAYS!*

*DON'T WORRY,* PRINCESS, THESE *STINGRAYS* ARE *FRIENDLY,* THEY *SAVED* OUR *LIVES.*

*"SOON...*

*THANKS,* GUYS! WE WOULDN'T HAVE MADE IT *WITHOUT YOU!*

ARE YOU *ALL RIGHT,* PRINCESS?

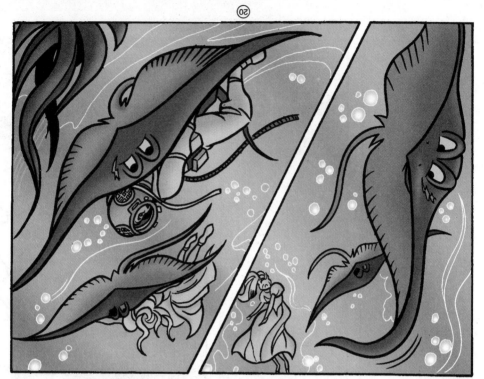

"...FIRST..."

"...AND AS SOON AS I GET THIS SUIT OFF..."

"...I'LL BE ABLE TO SWIM TO THE SURFACE... AND JOIN YOU..."

"...IF I... DON'T RUN OUT ...OF AIR..."

"THAT'S IT, PENELOPE. SWIM TO THE SURFACE..."

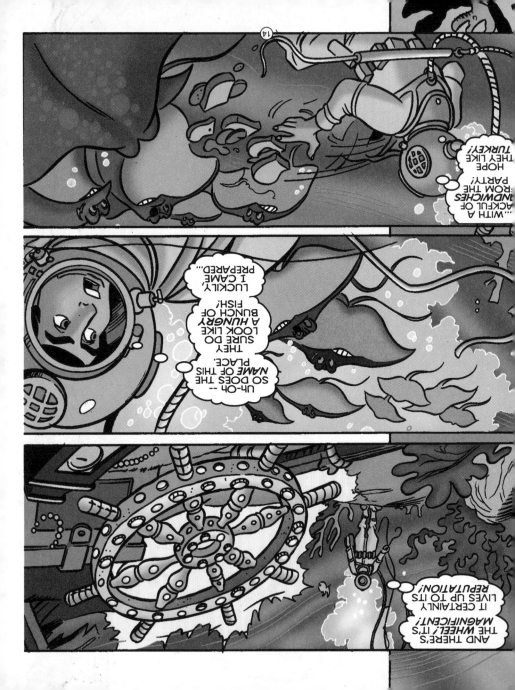

BUT FIRST THINGS *FIRST*.

KING HAROLD, I HAVE *NO* DESIRE TO DO *ANY HARM* TO YOUR BELOVED DAUGHTER.

BELIEVE ME, MY GREATEST DESIRE IS TO *RETURN* HER TO YOU, SAFE AND SOUND.

ALL YOU HAVE TO DO IS GIVE ME A SMALL *TOKEN* IN *RETURN*...

ANY MAN *FOOLISH* ENOUGH TO TRY TO RECOVER THE WHEEL WOULD BE *RIPPED* TO *PIECES* BY THE *STINGRAYS* DOWN THERE!

IN *THAT* CASE, SAY GOODBYE TO YOUR LOVELY DAUGHTER. YOU'LL NEVER SEE HER *AGAIN!*

LOOKS LIKE THE *WEDDING* IS OFF.

IF ONLY *MARRYING* HER WAS MY *ONLY DUTY* AS PRINCE...

"...I'LL SHOW THEM WHAT HAPPENS TO PEOPLE WITHOUT INVITATIONS!"

APPARENTLY, THE CAPTAIN AND HIS CREW HAVE DECIDED TO COME ASHORE -- AT LEAST LONG ENOUGH TO ATTEND YOUR PARTY.

CAPTAIN CUTLASS! HE'S THE MOST NOTORIOUS PIRATE SAILING THE SEVEN SEAS!

AND I SUGGEST YOU AND YOUR GUESTS REMAIN STILL -- OR I'LL HAVE MY MEN SKEWER THE WHOLE SCURVY LOT OF YOU!

THE NAME IS CAPTAIN CUTLASS, M'LORD.

UNHAND MY DAUGHTER, SCOUNDREL!

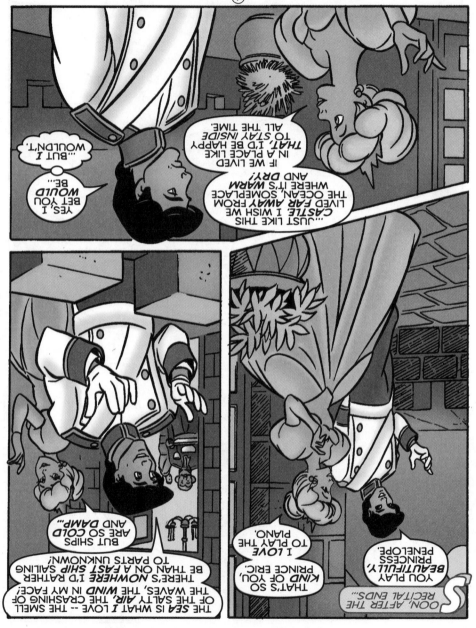

# DISNEY'S
# THE 🐚 LITTLE
# MERMAID

## "UNDERWATER ENGAGEMENTS"
### PART TWO: ERIC'S STORY

| | |
|---|---|
| **BOB BUDIANSKY**<br>WRITER | **JOSÉ DELBO**<br>PENCILER |
| **GARY FIELDS**<br>**STEVE GEORGE**<br>**SCOTT MCCRAE**<br>INKERS | **TWILIGHT GRAPHICS**<br>COLORISTS |
| | **COMICRAFT'S DAVE LAMPHEAR**<br>LETTERER |
| **HARVEY RICHARDS III**<br>ART CORRECTIONIST | **EVAN SKOLNICK**<br>EDITOR |
| **GREGG SANDERSON**<br>ASSOCIATE EDITOR | **FABIAN NICIEZA**<br>EDITOR-IN-CHIEF |

**DISNEY'S THE LITTLE MERMAID: "UNDERWATER ENGAGEMENTS"** Vol. I, No.1 © 1997 Disney Enterprises, Inc. Published by Acclaim Books, a division of Acclaim Comics, Inc., Fabian Nicieza, President. Office of Publication: 275 Seventh Avenue, New York, NY 10001. Reproduction in whole or in part without written permission from the copyright owner is strictly forbidden. No similarities between any of the names, characters, persons and/or institutions in this magazine with those of any persons living or dead, or any institution is intended and any similarity which may exist is purely coincidental. Acclaim Books and logo is a registered trademark of Acclaim Comics, Inc. ISBN 1-57840-242-5. Printed in the United States of America